Skills Builders

Grammar and Punctuation

YEAR 4

Maddy Barnes

RISING STARS

Rising Stars UK Ltd, 7 Hatchers Mews, Bermondsey Street, London SE1 3GS
www.risingstars-uk.com

Every effort has been made to trace copyright holders and obtain their permission for the use of copyright materials. The publishers will gladly receive information enabling them to rectify any error or omission in subsequent editions.

All facts are correct at time of going to press.

Published 2013
Reprinted 2013, 2014
Text, design and layout © 2013 Rising Stars UK Ltd

Project manager: Dawn Booth
Editorial: Sue Walton
Proofreader: Margaret Crowther
Design: Words & Pictures Ltd, London
Cover design: Amina Dudhia
Acknowledgements: p.7 iStock/Nathalie Beauvois; p.8 iStock/Elena Nayashkova; p.10 iStock/piart; p.11 (top) iStock/kysa; p.11 (bottom) iStock/CandO_Designs; p.12 iStock/Frank Ramspott; p.13 iStock/Christian Tőlg; p.14 iStock/William Bacon; p.15 (top) iStock/rudall30; p.15 (bottom) iStock/Milorad Zaric; p.17 iStock/Yael Weiss; p.20 iStock/rikidoh; p.21 iStock/MolinaDesign; p.22 iStock/CurvaBezier; p.28 iStock/João Lourenço; p.29 iStock/Maria Holdren; p.30 iStock/Andera Jacobs; p.31 iStock/Larry Rains; p.32 iStock/exxorian; p.36 iStock/Servet Gürbüz (use G&P Y3 p37); p.40 iStock/Kateryna Davydenko; p.41 iStock/Oleksiy Tsuper

British Library Cataloguing-in-Publication Data
A CIP record for this book is available from the British Library.

ISBN: 978-0-85769-695-3
Printed in Singapore by Craft Print International

Skills Builders: Grammar and Punctuation

YEAR 4

Contents

* Revision pages

What we have included:

1 Each unit covers aspects of grammar and punctuation taken from the new National Curriculum framework.

2 The units at the beginning of the book focus on basic skills which pupils should recognise from their previous learning and set mini challenges to encourage pupils to recap what they already know. These are often 'Warming up' questions, which are also used to test just learned knowledge throughout the book.

3 Other sections introduce new skills which are organised in a 'Getting hotter' section and some push even further in the 'Burn it up!' section.

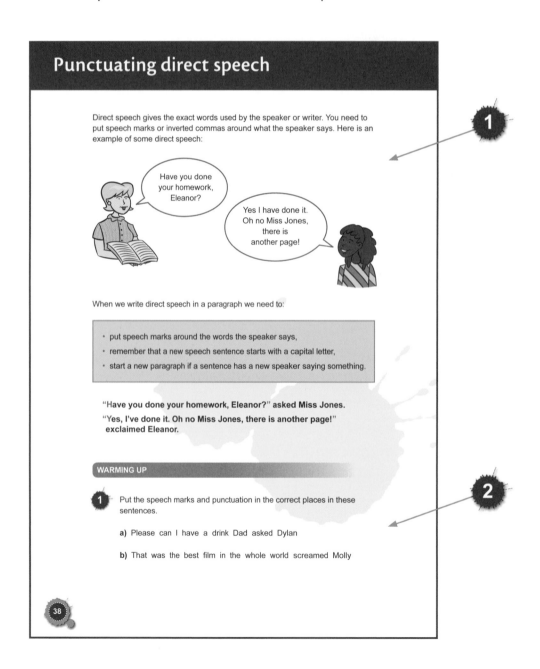

Punctuating direct speech

Direct speech gives the exact words used by the speaker or writer. You need to put speech marks or inverted commas around what the speaker says. Here is an example of some direct speech:

Have you done your homework, Eleanor?

Yes I have done it. Oh no Miss Jones, there is another page!

When we write direct speech in a paragraph we need to:

- put speech marks around the words the speaker says,
- remember that a new speech sentence starts with a capital letter,
- start a new paragraph if a sentence has a new speaker saying something.

"Have you done your homework, Eleanor?" asked Miss Jones.

"Yes, I've done it. Oh no Miss Jones, there is another page!" exclaimed Eleanor.

WARMING UP

1 Put the speech marks and punctuation in the correct places in these sentences.

a) Please can I have a drink Dad asked Dylan

b) That was the best film in the whole world screamed Molly

38

4

How to use this book

4 At the end of each section is a 'How did I do?' assessment for learning where pupils can record how well they did.

5 There are assessment points throughout the book titled 'Assess and review', which allow opportunities for pupils to recap new learning in small steps.

6 The correct grammatical terminology is used throughout this book to encourage acquisition of technical language.

7 All answers are included so pupils can check on their progress.

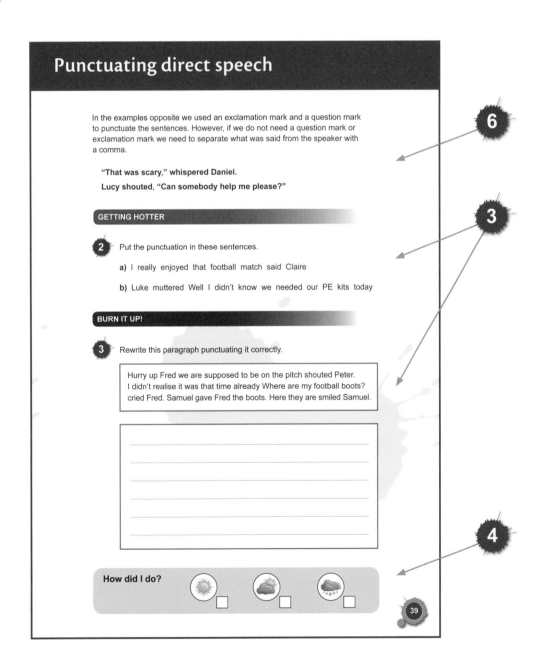

Identifying word classes

Words are organised into different classes.

Nouns	Adjectives	Verbs
Tell you the names of people, places, feelings and things.	Tell you more about the noun.	Tell you what is happening in the sentence (sometimes referred to as **action words**).
David table cat happiness Spain	huge fluffy cute blue tall	walks sang breaths wrote think

WARMING UP

 1 Sort these words into the correct categories.

Emma   kick   sticky   Vincent

drives   France   strange   thin

stadium   Manchester   giggled

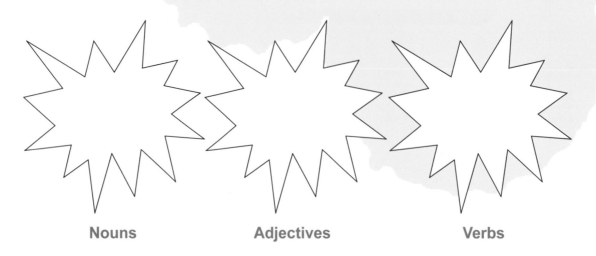

Nouns   Adjectives   Verbs

How did I do?

Using adverbs

When we read, we create pictures in our heads. Adverbs help us to fill in the background and explore things.

how?	when?	where?
happily	yesterday	outside
quickly	now	everywhere

Adverbs can be fun – we can change the meaning of a whole sentence just by changing the adverb.

The children were working **quietly**.

The children were working **noisily**.

WARMING UP

 1 Use another adverb from the one in brackets to complete the sentence.

> **a)** Carla walked (**quickly**) .... to the library.
>
> **b)** Shaun (**gently**) .... stroked the cat.
>
> **c)** I'm going (**outside**) .... to eat my lunch.
>
> **d)** They all ran (**uphill**) ....

Choosing a or an

All the letters in the alphabet are either vowels or consonants.

Vowels	a e i o u
Consonants	b c d f g h j k l m n p q r s t v w x y z

When adding **a** or **an** we need to apply the rules below.

a	an
When words begin with a consonant.	When words begin with a vowel.
a girl a rabbit a pencil a street a house	an elephant an igloo an apple an umbrella an orange

WARMING UP

 1 Choose **a** or **an** to complete the sentences.

> **a)** Maria and John took .... picnic to the park.
>
> **b)** Noah had .... banana for his lunch.
>
> **c)** Alyssa dropped .... ice cube onto the floor.
>
> **d)** Mark saw .... eagle soaring in the sky.
>
> **e)** Pam bought .... new dress.
>
> **f)** Luke won .... award for cross-country running.
>
> **g)** Ellie drew .... amazing unicorn.
>
> **h)** Ahmed wanted .... cream cake
> for dessert.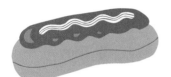

How did I do?   ☐   ☐   ☐

Using apostrophes for contraction

Sometimes we shorten words. When we do this we use an apostrophe to show where letters have been missed out. This is called using an apostrophe for contraction.

cannot ➔ **can't**

we will ➔ **we'll**

 1   Use what you know to write the two words which match each contraction.

I'm   =   I   +   am

a) don't   = _____ + _____

b) I'll   = _____ + _____

c) should've   = _____ + _____

d) you're   = _____ + _____

e) it's   = _____ + _____

How did I do?   ☐   ☐   ☐

Adding prefixes

A **prefix** is added at the beginning of a word to make another word.

un-	dis-	mis-	super-	anti-	re-
decided	appear	placed	hero	clockwise	cycle
undecided	disappear	misplaced	superhero	anticlockwise	recycle

1   Some of these words are nonsense words and some are real. Circle all the words which are real words.

disappoint   mistable   antibiotic

replay   undo   supersnow

discover   antidog   misbehave

reassure

dispicture   supernatural

antiseptic

rego   misadventure

2. Now use the real words to write a sentence on the back of your sheet.

How did I do?

 ☐   ☐   ☐

Using determiners

A **determiner** stands before a noun and any other words which explain the noun.

Some of the most common determiners are:

the, a, an, this, my, her, his, your, both, another, neither, either, other, all, those, which, this.

1 Read the following and put a tick (✓) next to the phrase if it is correct and a cross (✗) if not.

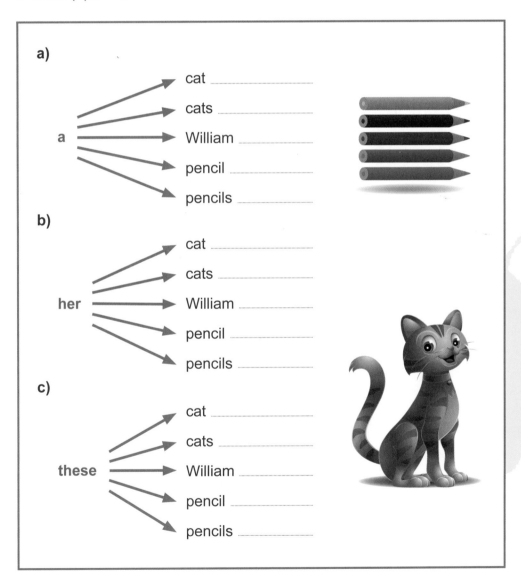

a)

cat ....

cats ....

a → William ....

pencil ....

pencils ....

b)

cat ....

cats ....

her → William ....

pencil ....

pencils ....

c)

cat ....

cats ....

these → William ....

pencil ....

pencils ....

How did I do?

 ☐   ☐   ☐

11

Using time conjunctions

Time conjunctions are used to show that time is passing or has passed.

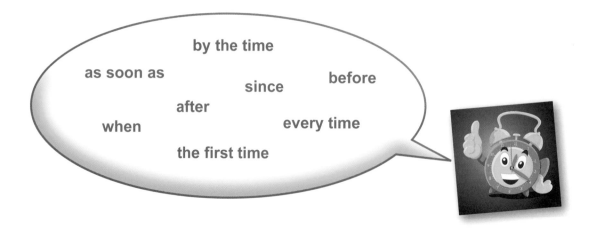

 Use all the words in each table to build a sentence.

a) By the time ....

....

Mary	cake	the
ready	realised	was
burned.	had	it

b) As soon as ....

....

arrived	in	he
Ibiza	Luke	the
pool.	in	jumped

How did I do?

 ☐   ☐   ☐

12

Using prepositions

A **preposition** links a noun or pronoun to another word in the sentence. The preposition usually tells the reader where the object is.

WARMING UP

 1 Choose a preposition to complete the sentences.

a) She spends all day _____ the house.

b) You should come around _____ Sunday.

c) We travelled _____ plane.

d) Meishan sat _____ to Thewni.

e) I met her _____ 3 p.m.

next

on

in

at

by

GETTING HOTTER

2 Complete the following prepositions:

a) und __ __

b) bene __ __ __

c) dur __ __ __

d) exc __ __ __

How did I do?

 ☐   ☐   ☐

Organising your writing

All writing needs to be organised so that the reader can understand what is written. There are many different ways to organise our thoughts, ideas and writing.

Starting a new paragraph shows the reader that the character, place, topic or time may have changed.

WARMING UP

 1 Read the paragraph openers below and write **C** if a new character is introduced, **P** for place and **T** for time. For example:

Three weeks later   **T**

---

a) Meanwhile, in another city ....

b) Not long after ....

c) A dark figure appeared at the window ....

d) As they entered the overgrown forest ....

e) Later that day ....

f) A pair of eyes looked back through the letterbox ....

g) The bright lights welcomed them into the hall ....

h) In 2015 ....

How did I do?   ☐   ☐   ☐

Punctuating direct speech

We use speech marks or inverted commas " " to punctuate direct speech.

"Fee-fi-fo-fum, I smell the blood of an Englishman!"
screeched the Giant.

 1 Use direct speech to write a sentence including what each character is saying.

a) ....

....

....

b) ....

....

....

How did I do?

15

Using pronouns accurately

When we write sentences we need to use pronouns to vary the subject. Pronouns replace nouns. Here are some pronouns:

me, him, his, she, he, her, who, what, that.

WARMING UP

 1 Match the group of words on the left with the correct pronoun.

Dawn and Imran
a) Danny
b) Annie
c) Pam and I
d) the taxi

it
we
they
he
she

GETTING HOTTER

2 Underline the pronouns in this list of words.

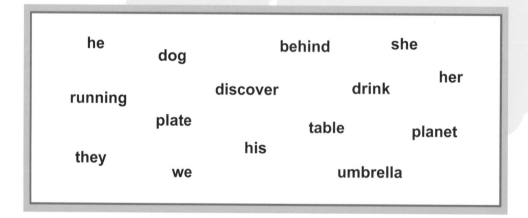

he   dog   behind   she

running   discover   drink   her

plate   table   planet

they   his   we   umbrella

How did I do?

 ☐   ☐   ☐

Using the present perfect tense

When we want to write about something that has happened in the past, but we do not specify the time, we use the **present perfect tense**.

Have you ever **met** the Queen?

We add the verb **have**.

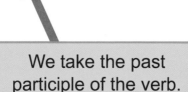

We take the past participle of the verb.

WARMING UP

 Complete the following sentences using the present perfect tense.

I **have been** a teacher for 12 years.

a) He _____ never _____ tennis.

b) _____ you _____ the book yet?

c) She _____ not _____ her dinner yet.

d) They _____ _____ the film already.

e) We _____ _____ here for ten years.

How did I do?

 ☐   ☐   ☐

17

Using time links to sequence

We can use time links to show the passage of time in fiction and retellings. We can vary which time links we use so that they guide the reader.

Open the story	Show time is passing	Ending the story
One rainy morning Once upon a time	After that Soon after Before he realised	At last At the end of the day

 1 Sort these time links into the described categories in the table above.

Last Wednesday   Eventually   Meanwhile

In a flash   On 12th December
                Finally

After he had gone   Then   It all began

How did I do?   ☐   ☐   ☐

18

Assess and review

 1 Show how we use the apostrophe for contraction in the following sentences.

> **a)** "No you (**cannot**) _____ have another cake," Billy.
>
> **b)** I really (**do not**) _____ want to go to the park today.
>
> **c)** (**I am**) _____ having a brilliant time at this party.
>
> **d)** He (**will not**) _____ give the ball back to her.
>
> **e)** (**It is**) _____ my birthday today.

GETTING HOTTER

2 Add **a** or **an** to complete these sentences:

> **a)** I have an apple and _____ orange for my lunch.
>
> **b)** I need to buy a present and _____ card for my Mum.
>
> **c)** Do you know where I can get _____ umbrella from?
>
> **d)** _____ Eskimo lives in an igloo.
>
> **e)** I had _____ egg with toast for my breakfast.
>
> **f)** I wanted _____ football for my birthday present.

How did I do?   ☐   ☐   ☐

Using the future tense

Verbs can be written in different tenses. The past tense describes something that has already happened. The present tense is what is happening right now. The future tense refers to what will happen in the future.

Past tense: The dog **ran** to the park.

Present tense: The dog **runs** to the park.

Future tense: The dog **will run** to the park.

When we write in the future tense we add **will** or **shall** to the infinitive part of the verb.

I **will see** you next weekend.

Alex King **will be** the top goal scorer next season.

I **will finish** reading my book tonight.

My Dad **will bring** chocolates home on Thursday night.

WARMING UP

 1 Identify the infinitive form of the verb and complete the table below.

Infinitive form	Present tense	Past tense
to walk	walks	walked
	sings	sang
	thinks	thought
	plays	played

Using the future tense

Luke **will cook** an amazing meal next Saturday.

Using will + infinitive of verb

I **shall fix** the shed door tomorrow.

Using shall + infinitive of verb

2 Change the sentences below from the present tense to the future.

The girl sings in the hall.

The girl **will sing** in the hall.

a) Meera is running in the park.

_____

b) Carla is eating her grapes.

_____

c) John is playing football.

_____

d) Alison is drawing a picture.

_____

How did I do? ☐ ☐ ☐

Adding -er and -est

Comparatives are adjectives we use when we want to compare two people, places or things. We usually make a comparative adjective by adding **-er** to the end of the adjective. For example:

long	+	**-er**	=	longer
slow	+	**-er**	=	slower
thin	+	**-er**	=	thinner

1 Add **-er** to the following words:

a) tall + **-er** = ...

b) loud + **-er** = ...

c) small + **-er** = ...

d) hard + **-er** = ...

e) soft + **-er** = ...

When we want to compare three or more things we can make an adjective into a superlative adjective by adding **-est** to the ending and adding **the** in front of the adjective. For example:

Anthony is loud.

Ali is loud**er**.

Olivia is **the** loud**est**.

Answers

Skills Builders

Grammar and Punctuation

YEAR
4

Maddy Barnes

Identifying word classes (page 6)

1 *Nouns:* Emma, stadium, France, Manchester, Vincent

Adjectives: sticky, thin, strange   *Verbs:* kick, giggled, drives

Using adverbs (page 7)

1 Answers will vary

a) Carla walked slowly to the library.

b) Shaun tentatively stroked the cat.

c) I'm going inside to eat my lunch.

d) Thay all ran downhill.

Choosing a or an (page 8)

1 **a)** a **b)** a **c)** an **d)** an **e)** a **f)** an **g)** an **h)** a

Using apostrophes for contraction (page 9)

1 **a)** do + not

b) I + will

c) should + have

d) you + are

e) it + is

Adding prefixes (page 10)

1 disappoint, antibiotic, replay, undo, discover, misbehave, supernatural, reassure, antiseptic, misadventure

Using determiners (page 11)

1 **a)** cat ✓ cats ✗ William ✗ pencil ✓ pencils ✗

b) cat ✓ cats ✓ William ✗ pencil ✓ pencils ✓

c) cat ✗ cats ✓ William ✗ pencil ✗ pencils ✓

Using time conjunctions (page 12)

1 **a)** By the time the cake was ready Mary realised it had burned. or
By the time Mary realised the cake was ready it had burned.

b) As soon as Luke arrived in Ibiza he jumped in the pool.
As soon as he arrived in Ibiza Luke jumped in the pool.

Using prepositions (page 13)

1 **a)** in

b) on

c) by

d) next

e) at

2 **a)** under

b) beneath

c) during

d) except

Organising your writing (page 14)

1 **a)** P **b)** T **c)** C **d)** P **e)** T **f)** C **g)** P **h)** T

Punctuating direct speech (page 15)

1 Answers will vary

a) "I'll huff and I'll puff and I'll blow your house down!" screamed the wolf.

b) "Somebody has broken my chair!" sobbed the bear.

Using pronouns accurately (page 16)

1 **a)** he

b) she

c) we

d) It

2 he, she, they, we, her, his

Using the present perfect tense (page 17)

1 Answers will vary

a) He has never played tennis.

b) Have you read the book yet?

c) She has not had her dinner yet.

d) They have seen the film already.

e) We have lived here for ten years.

Using time links to sequence (page 18)

1 *Opening:* Last Wednesday, On 12th December, It all began

Time passing: Meanwhile, In a flash, After he had gone, Then

Ending: Finally, Eventually

Assess and review (page 19)

1 **a)** can't

b) don't

c) I'm

d) won't

e) it's

2 **a)** an

b) a

c) an

d) An

e) an

f) a

Using the future tense (pages 20–21)

1 to sing, to think, to play

2 **a)** Meera will run in the park.

b) Carla will eat her grapes.

c) John will play football.

d) Alison will draw a picture.

Adding -er and -est (pages 22–23)

1 a) taller
 b) louder
 c) smaller
 d) harder
 e) softer

2 a) quieter / the quietest
 b) braver / the bravest
 c) darker / the darkest
 d) smoother / the smoothest
 e) lighter / the lightest
 f) tougher / the toughest

3 a) Laura is small and Claire is even smaller, but Faye is the smallest.
 b) Julie is rich and Wendy is even richer, but Amanda is the richest.
 c) Renato is tall and Richard is taller, but Aminaa is the tallest.
 d) Zoe is fast and Lindsey is faster, but Emma is the fastest.

Subordinate clauses (page 25)

1 a) Before
 b) Although
 c) but
 d) until

Changing singular nouns to plural nouns (page 26)

1 a) watches
 b) candles
 c) branches
 d) dishes
 e) balloons
 f) apples
 g) clocks
 h) lunches
 i) mice

Proper nouns and collective nouns (page 27)

1 *Proper nouns:* India, Ali, William, Fiona, Pakistan
 Collective nouns: herd, class, swarm, flock, shoal

Using did, done, was and were (pages 28–29)

1 a) done b) did c) did d) done e) done

2 a) I have did it before. ✗
 b) My Mum done it for me. ✗
 c) They did it earlier. ✓
 d) She done it first. ✗

3 a) was
 b) were
 c) were
 d) was
 e) were

4 a) was
 b) did
 c) were
 d) Did
 e) Was
 f) done

Choosing nouns or pronouns appropriately (pages 30–31)

1 He, He, them

2 a) Some, others
 b) Both
 c) Most / All
 d) Neither
 e) any
 f) some
 g) Most / All / Many

Fronted adverbials (pages 32–33)

1 a) During the night
 b) Since it is so late
 c) While I was waiting for the train
 d) If I have time

2 Every time Eleanor closed her eyes, she imagined she was a princess.

3 In November, the weather is usually colder than September.
 Because you arrived early, you can sit wherever you like.
 During the lesson, the girls wrote notes to each other.
 While he was talking, he scratched his head nervously.

Assess and review (pages 34–35)

1 a) I will go swimming on Monday.
 b) It will rain when we are in Wales.
 c) Alex will score five goals in the football match.
 d) Dad will clean the windows this morning.

2 a) wealthier / wealthiest
 b) tall / tallest
 c) scary / scarier
 d) bright / brighter
 e) hot / hottest

3 a) swarm
 b) litter
 c) herd
 d) pack
 e) block
 f) box
 g) bouquet (accept bunch)
 h) ream

4 but, before, whilst, however, so, if, until, since

Organising paragraphs around a theme (page 36)

1 Answers will vary

    P: Schools are places pupils go to be educated.

    E: All pupils have the opportunity to go to school in the UK.

    E: Throughout British history, schools have not always offered a free education. Instead some schools charged a lot of money so many children did not go to school at all.

Punctuating direct speech (pages 38–39)

1 a) "Please can I have a drink Dad?" asked Dylan.

    b) "That was the best film in the whole world!" screamed Molly.

2 a) "I really enjoyed that football match," said Claire.

    b) Luke muttered, "Well I didn't know we needed our PE kits today!"

3 "Hurry up Fred, we are supposed to be on the pitch!" shouted Peter.

    "I didn't realise it was that time already. Where are my football boots?" cried Fred.

    Samuel gave Fred the boots.

    "Here they are," smiled Samuel.

Apostrophes for singular and plural possession (pages 40–41)

1 a) the boy's pencil

    b) the pen's lid

    c) the man's phone

    d) the woman's seat

    e) the girl's ball

    f) the rabbit's burrow

    g) the bird's nest

2 a) the book's pages

    b) the children's pencils

    c) the girls' bags (accept girl's)

    d) Rachel's bike

    e) the tree's branches (accept trees')

    f) the women's hats

    g) the dogs' leads (accept dog's)

    h) Ellie's purse

Assess and review (pages 43–44)

1 a) "This is the best party I have ever been to," shouted Faye.

    b) "Would anybody like a drink?" asked Mum.

    c) "What a beautiful ring," exclaimed Catherine.

    d) "I am hoping to finish my work by this evening," said Dermot.

    e) "Can I copy your homework please?" whispered Laura.

    f) "Wahey, this football match has been amazing!" screamed Wendy.

    g) "I don't believe it. It is still raining," grumbled Pauline.

2 a) P b) S c) S d) S e) P f) S g) S

3 a) We were playing in the park all day.

    b) Yesterday, she had a great birthday party.

    c) They will be going to the cinema next week.

    d) He had a pizza for his tea last night.

    e) We will have a brilliant time at the disco tomorrow.

    f) I took the chocolate cake around to Gran's last week.

    g) Tomorrow we will make a model at school.

    h) She said she didn't want to eat her lunch.

    i) I came back at 7 p.m. yesterday.

    j) You are a clever girl Minadi.

Adding -er and -est

2 Write the comparative and superlative forms of the following adjectives.

	Comparative	Superlative
a) quiet		
b) brave		
c) dark		
d) smooth		
e) light		
f) tough		

BURN IT UP!

3 Complete these sentences so that they make sense. (Don't forget to add **the** when you need to.)

a) Laura is small and Claire is even _____ , but Faye is

_____ _____ .

b) Julie is rich and Wendy is even _____ , but Amanda is

_____ _____ .

c) Renato is tall and Richard is _____ , but Aminaa is

_____ _____ .

d) Zoe is fast and Lindsey is _____ , but Emma is

_____ _____ .

How did I do?

23

Subordinate clauses

A **clause** is a single idea or event which has a subject, one verb and may contain further detail. As long as there is only one verb, there is only one clause. For example:

> One bright sunny morning, the beautiful princess Medeeha wandered through the deep, overgrown forest.

A **subordinate clause** expresses one idea but does not make sense on its own. A subordinate clause needs a main clause to complete the sense. The main and subordinate clauses go together to make a complex sentence.

subordinate clause   main clause

When she wandered through the forest, Medeeha felt nervous because it had been a scary moment.

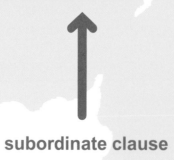

subordinate clause

Subordinate clauses

We can create subordinate clauses in different ways:

➤ we can begin a clause with **when**, **while**, **before**, **after**, **since**, **until**, **if**, **because**, **although**, **as**

➤ we can use **but**, **and**, **or**, **so**, to join two simple sentences.

When he got up, Billy ran to the front door to get his birthday cards.

Billy got up **and** ran to the front door to get his birthday cards.

WARMING UP

 1 Complete each of these sentences using one of the **red** or **green** words above.

a) .... she went to school, Hope dressed her younger sister Poppy.

b) .... he worked really hard, Grant enjoyed having fun with his friends.

c) Louisa wanted to read her book .... she couldn't find it.

d) The old ladies waited patiently at the bus stop .... the bus finally arrived.

How did I do? ☐ ☐ ☐

Changing singular nouns to plural nouns

When we make regular nouns plural we add -s.

dog	+	-s	=	dog**s**
book	+	-s	=	book**s**
girl	+	-s	=	girl**s**

However, if the noun ends with these letters we add **-es**:

s	z	ch	sh	x
buses	buzzes	beaches	brushes	foxes

There are also some nouns which are irregular and have different endings. For example:

man	becomes	**men**,
person	becomes	**people**,
thief	becomes	**thieves**.

WARMING UP

 1 Write the plural for each of the following nouns.

table   **tables**   e) balloon _____

a) watch _____   f) apple _____

b) candle _____   g) clock _____

c) branch _____   h) lunch _____

d) dish _____   i) mouse _____

How did I do?

 ☐   ☐   ☐

26

Proper nouns and collective nouns

Proper nouns are the names of people, places, nationalities, languages, days of the week and months. We write proper nouns with a capital letter. For example: **November, Wednesday, French, David, Manchester.**

Collective nouns are the names given to a group of people, animals or things. They do not need a capital letter. Here are some collective nouns: team, group, crowd, class.

WARMING UP

 1   Read the nouns and sort them into the correct categories. You will need to rewrite the proper nouns with capital letters.

india   william   fiona   ali   herd   class   flock   swarm   shoal   pakistan

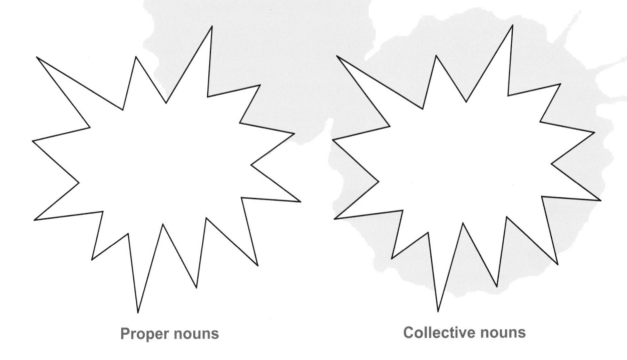

Proper nouns   Collective nouns

How did I do?   ☐   ☐   ☐

Using did, done, was and were

Did or done?

Sometimes we confuse **did** and **done** and find it difficult to decide when to use them.

We **did** all of our work – simple past tense.

He **has** already **done** his work – present perfect tense.

We **have done** many things – present perfect tense.

No one **had done** that before – past perfect tense.

WARMING UP

1 Write **did** or **done** in the following sentences.

a) Have you _____ your homework?

b) I _____ the very best I could.

c) She wants to know who _____ this.

d) Billy has _____ his best today.

e) What have you _____ with your money?

GETTING HOTTER

2 Place a tick by the sentences which are correct and a cross by those which do not make sense.

a) I have did it before. _____

b) My Mum done it for me. _____

c) They did it earlier. _____

d) She done it first. _____

Using did, done, was and were

She **was** ready for school.

They **were** ready for school.

WARMING UP

 3   Complete these sentences using **was** or **were**.

a) It _____ almost time to go home.

b) They _____ waiting for a long time at the bus stop.

c) The boys _____ all playing together at lunch time.

d) I _____ only joking with you.

e) Kaleem and Tommy _____ playing tennis after school.

GETTING HOTTER

 4   Choose **did**, **done**, **was** or **were** to complete these sentences.

a) It _____ her birthday last Monday.

b) She _____ it before she went to bed.

c) The girls _____ excited about the concert.

d) _____ you ask for a drink?

e) _____ it busy in town today?

f) The teacher did not know they had _____ it before.

How did I do?

 ☐   ☐   ☐

Choosing nouns or pronouns appropriately

Using the same noun more than once in a sentence often sounds repetitive and awkward. We can use pronouns to avoid this.

> **My brother** loves **football**. **My brother** says **football** is the best game **my brother** has ever played.

If we change the nouns **brother** and **football** to pronouns the sentences are much better.

> **My brother** loves football. **He** says **it** is the best game **he** has ever played.

WARMING UP

 1 Read the following extract and then rewrite it changing the nouns to pronouns.

> Billy **loves** cookies. Billy **especially loves chocolate and double chocolate** cookies. Billy **would do anything for** cookies!

Billy **loves cookies.** .... especially loves chocolate and

double chocolate cookies. .... would do anything for

.... !

Choosing nouns or pronouns appropriately

To vary sentences in both fiction and non-fiction texts, we can choose pronouns to be more precise. There are many pronouns which can be used to introduce new ideas, compare ideas and replace nouns.

Here are some pronouns:

some	none		any
all		more	
both	many		most
	few	others	
neither	less	each	either

GETTING HOTTER

2   Choose a pronoun from the word bank above to complete each sentence.

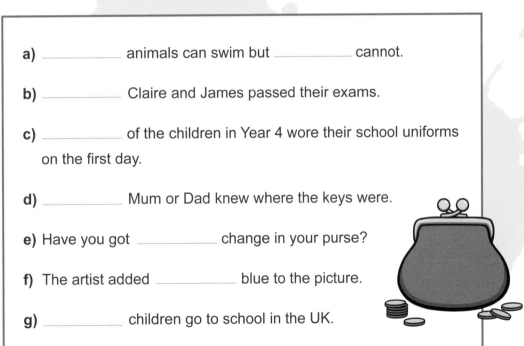

a) .... animals can swim but .... cannot.

b) .... Claire and James passed their exams.

c) .... of the children in Year 4 wore their school uniforms on the first day.

d) .... Mum or Dad knew where the keys were.

e) Have you got .... change in your purse?

f) The artist added .... blue to the picture.

g) .... children go to school in the UK.

How did I do?   ☐   ☐   ☐

Fronted adverbials

We can use adverbial phrases at the beginning of a sentences. These are called **fronted adverbials** and are used for different reasons. They may add more information about time or place or they may offer a reason.

Adverb of time	Adverb of place	Adverb of reason
While I was,	In the north of England,	Since it is so late,
Every time she,	In the middle of the forest.	Because you arrived late,

Notice that you usually need to put a comma after the fronted adverbial as it is an adverbial phrase.

WARMING UP

 1 Underline the fronted adverbials in these sentences.

<u>In the north of England</u>, **there are many popular football teams.**

a) During the night, the rabbits escaped from their hutches.

b) Since it is so late, you need to go to bed without having anything to eat.

c) While I was waiting for the train, it began to snow.

d) If I have time, I will read you another story.

Fronted adverbials

So, fronted adverbials are adverbial phrases or clauses which are positioned at the beginning of the sentence. They are usually followed by a comma.

GETTING HOTTER

 2 Rewrite this sentence and insert the comma after the fronted adverbial.

> **Every time Eleanor closed her eyes she imagined she was a princess.**

BURN IT UP!

 3 Match a fronted adverbial with a sentence ending to make a new sentence which makes sense.

Slowly, he walked to the front of the hall.

Slowly,	you can sit wherever you like.
In November,	he scratched his head nervously.
Because you arrived early,	the girls wrote notes to each other.
During the lesson,	he walked to the front of the hall.
While he was talking,	the weather is usually colder than September.

How did I do?   ☐   ☐   ☐

Assess and review

1 Change these sentences to the future tense.

a) I went swimming on Monday.

....

b) It rained today when we were in Wales.

....

c) Alex scored five goals in the football match.

....

d) Dad cleaned the windows this morning.

....

2 Complete the following adjectives. Watch out – some are irregular!

short	shorter	shortest
a) wealthy	....	....
b)	taller	....
c)	....	scariest
d)	....	brightest
e)	hotter	....

Assess and review

3 Find out these collective nouns.

a) a .... of bees

b) a .... of kittens

c) a .... of cattle

d) a .... of wolves

e) a .... of flats

f) a .... of tricks

g) a .... of flowers

h) a .... of paper

4 Circle the words below which can be used to begin a subordinate clause.

apple   before   table

but

if   paper

house   he   what   on

girl   until   whilst   of

so   since   however

How did I do?

 ☐ ☐ ☐

Organising paragraphs around a theme

We organise our writing into paragraphs so that:

➤ the text is easier to read,

➤ the text shows changes in time, place, people,

➤ the text is presented in the appropriate way.

A paragraph needs to be built up accurately. In order to write a detailed paragraph in non-fiction we can apply the **PEE** strategy – make a **P**oint, **E**xplain your point and **E**xpand or offer some evidence.

For example:

P Lions are often considered to be the 'kings of the jungle'.

E This may be because lions are at the top of the food chain and are feared by many other animals.

E Historically lions have been thought to be both brave and courageous.

WARMING UP

 1 Choose your own theme and apply **PEE**.

P ......

E ......

E ......

How did I do?

 ☐   ☐   ☐

Different ways to separate your writing

Paragraphs are one way to separate our ideas and present our writing. Writing can also be presented in other ways.

For example:

This is a text box.
Text boxes separate writing clearly for the reader.

This is a thought bubble.
Thought bubbles are used to show ideas or what a character is thinking in their head.

This is a speech bubble.
Speech bubbles are used to show what a character is saying out loud.

Punctuating direct speech

Direct speech gives the exact words used by the speaker or writer. You need to put speech marks or inverted commas around what the speaker says. Here is an example of some direct speech:

When we write direct speech in a paragraph we need to:

- put speech marks around the words the speaker says,
- remember that a new speech sentence starts with a capital letter,
- start a new paragraph if a sentence has a new speaker saying something.

"Have you done your homework, Eleanor?" asked Miss Jones.

"Yes, I've done it. Oh no Miss Jones, there is another page!" exclaimed Eleanor.

 Put the speech marks and punctuation in the correct places in these sentences.

a) Please can I have a drink Dad asked Dylan

b) That was the best film in the whole world screamed Molly

Punctuating direct speech

In the examples opposite we used an exclamation mark and a question mark to punctuate the sentences. However, if we do not need a question mark or exclamation mark we need to separate what was said from the speaker with a comma.

"That was scary," whispered Daniel.

Lucy shouted, "Can somebody help me please?"

 Put the punctuation in these sentences.

a) I really enjoyed that football match said Claire

b) Luke muttered Well I didn't know we needed our PE kits today

 Rewrite this paragraph punctuating it correctly.

> Hurry up Fred we are supposed to be on the pitch shouted Peter.
> I didn't realise it was that time already Where are my football boots?
> cried Fred. Samuel gave Fred the boots. Here they are smiled Samuel.

How did I do?

An apostrophe can be used to show **possession**. This means that an apostrophe can be used to show who or what something belongs to. For example:

the **woman's** bag

Pam's glasses

Dermot's newspaper

the **bike's** wheel

 Use apostrophes to show possession.

the tail belonging to the cat = the cat's tail

a) the pencil belonging to the boy = ...

b) the lid belonging to the pen = ...

c) the phone belonging to the man = ...

d) the seat belonging to the woman = ...

e) the ball belonging to the girl = ...

f) the burrow belonging to the rabbit = ...

g) the nest belonging to the bird = ...

Apostrophes for singular and plural possession

If the owners are plural and end in **-s** (like **boys**), we just add an **apostrophe** after the **-s**. For example:

> The coats belonging to the boys = the boys' coats

If the owners are plural but don't end in **-s** like **men**, we add an **apostrophe** followed by an **-s**. For example:

> The cars belonging to the men = the men's cars.

GETTING HOTTER

 2 Rewrite these phrases to show possession. Add an **apostrophe** and **-s** (if you need to).

a) the book pages ....

b) the children pencils ....

c) the girls bags ....

d) Rachels bike ....

e) the tree branches ....

f) the womens hats ....

g) the dogs leads ....

h) Ellies purse ....

How did I do? ☐ ☐ ☐

Irregular verb families

Some of the verbs which we use the most in the English language are irregular (this means they do not follow a pattern like that of other verbs).

Some of these irregular verbs are: **be**, **have**, **do**, **say**, **make**, **go**, **take** and **come**.

To be

Present tense	Past tense
I am	I was
you are	you were
he/she/it is	he/she/it was
you are	you were
we are	we were
they are	they were

To have

Present tense	Past tense
I have	I had
you have	you had
he/she/it has	he/she/it had
you have	you had
we have	we had
they have	they had

Assess and review

 1 Add speech marks to the following sentences.

> **a)** This is the best party I have ever been to, shouted Faye.
>
> **b)** Would anybody like a drink? asked Mum.
>
> **c)** What a beautiful ring, exclaimed Catherine.
>
> **d)** I am hoping to finish my work by this evening, said Dermot.
>
> **e)** Can I copy your homework please? whispered Laura.
>
> **f)** Wahey, this football match has been amazing! screamed Wendy.
>
> **g)** I don't believe it. It is still raining, grumbled Pauline.

GETTING HOTTER

 2 Write **S** for singular and **P** for plural for each of these possessives.

> **a)** boys' ....
>
> **b)** cat's ....
>
> **c)** girl's ....
>
> **d)** table's ....
>
> **e)** teachers'............................
>
> **f)** car's ....
>
> **g)** woman's ....

Assess and review

3 There are some errors in the verbs in the sentences below. Read each
sentence and rewrite it so that it is correct.

a) We was playing in the park all day.

....

b) Yesterday, she have a great birthday party.

....

c) They were be going to the cinema next week.

....

d) He has a pizza for his tea last night.

....

e) We will had a brilliant time at the disco tomorrow.

....

f) I taken the chocolate cake around to Gran's last week.

....

g) Tomorrow we made a model at school.

....

h) She say she didn't want to eat her lunch.

....

i) I will come back at 7 p.m. yesterday.

....

j) You is a clever girl Minadi.

....

How did I do?   ☐   ☐   ☐